Written and illustrated by Lori Copeland
Project Design & Layout by Elizabeth Madden
Project Editing by Melissa Zace and Susan Bowman

ISBN 1-889636-13-4
Library of Congress Catalog No. 98-061529

10 9 8 7 6 5 4
Printed in the United States of America

Dedication

I gratefully dedicate this book to my family. To Tom, my husband and the person I most admire. To Katie and Jordan, God's most precious gift to me. To my parents, who gave me not only love and encouragement, but opportunity and character. And to Tom Sr. and Mary Nell, for love and prayers that have made a difference in my life.

I would also like to dedicate this book to all the "Hunters" who have challenged me to look at the world from a different perspective, and who make our lives a little more interesting and exciting with their gift of creativity, enthusiasm and the unexpected!

Acknowledgements

I wish to express my appreciation to those who made a valuable contribution to this work by providing opportunity, insight and encouragement.

Janet Denison
Dorene Morris
Pat Boland
Mike Stedham
Deanna Thomas
Cathey Casey
George Dawson

Trina Fink & the Bonham Group
Vickie Copeland
Janet Ardoyno
Ed Hallowell
Rick Fowler
Becky Cundiff & her Alta Vista
   fourth graders

Table of Contents

Part A: Hunter and His Amazing Remote Control Activity Guide 1

Introduction 3

How to Use this Material 7
   Channel Changer 9
      Distraction Game Test 10

   Pause 13
      The Pause Game 15
      Naming the Colors 16

   Fast Forward 17

   Rewind 19
      The Changing of the "Shoulds" Cards 22
      Famous Failures 26

   Slow Motion 27
      Feelings Vocabulary 29
      Matching Feeling with Experiences 30

   Coach 31
      The Coach's Playbook 33
      Divide and Organize 34
      Problem Solving Exercise 36

   Zapper 39
      Unhealthy Thinking 41
      Zap that Thought 42

   Way to Go! 45
      Letters of Affirmation 46

   A Message from Hunter 47

Reproducible Remote Control Covers 49

Part B: Hunter and His Amazing Remote Control Storybook 1

Hunter and His Amazing Remote Control

Part A: Activity Guide

A fun, hands-on way to teach self-control to ADHD children

Written & illustrated by Lori Copeland, Ph.D.

Introduction

In Focus

As a professional counselor working with children and adolescents, I am frequently confronted with the questions and concerns about attention deficit/hyperactivity disorder (ADHD). Despite a substantial number of resources available, parents, counselors, and teachers are still seeking practical and effective strategies for helping children who have difficulty with self-regulation. The common purpose is threefold: (1) behavior management, (2) social and academic, and (3) development of a healthy self-image. Those who engage daily in this collaborative effort encounter a number of issues emerging from the complexity and controversy surrounding diagnosis and treatment of ADHD. These issues are addressed in the following rationale for this book.

 The deficits in working memory characteristic of ADHD children, render many of the traditional cognitive behavioral approaches ineffective. These children frequently act too quickly to benefit from strategies that rely solely on self-instruction. The remote control approach teaches the child to use an external visual cue for self-regulation.

 Behavior management strategies implemented exclusively with the ADHD child, may contribute to social and physical isolation. Because the remote control approach is used with an entire class, it suggests to ADHD children that they are not the only ones who struggle with these behaviors and feelings; it normalizes these "problems" stressing that everyone has to work on self-control, self-esteem, and staying focused.

 Children benefit from the use of concrete examples to teach abstract concepts. The remote control approach uses an object that is very familiar to the typical child. The various buttons serve to consolidate multiple concepts related to behavior management. The metaphor of the remote control also bridges the gap between internal and external focus of control. Teaching children to assume responsibility for their behavior because "they are the only one who can make their remote control work" (see page 48 and SB 31).

 The frequent use of words and phrases related to behavior management may cause children to dislike or "tune-out" these statements. Replacing phrases like pay attention with put your channel on me can be a refreshing change in terminology for both the children and the teacher.

 Many of the current publications designed to help children to understand and cope with ADHD use the clinical diagnostic term as well as addressing the use of medication. These resources may not be useful for children with moderate symptoms who have not received a diagnosis or for ADHD children who are not taking medication. The "Hunter" book avoids direct references to this clinical information in an effort to reach a broader population of children who could benefit from this positive approach.

I initially used this book with individual clients and a small group of second and third graders at an elementary school. I developed activities to teach

4

and reinforce each of the remote control buttons. The program was then piloted in a forth grade class. In the following pages I will present my plan for using these concepts and activities. Teachers, counselors, and parents are encouraged to adapt this material to the age level and setting wherein it will be implemented. The activities have been designed for use in third and forth grade classes but can easily be modified for small group settings or other age groups. There are numerous ways the remote control concept can be used by creative professionals. It is my hope that this program will empower children with ADHD and those who work with them with new tools for success both inside and outside of the classroom.

Each student should have a remote control made with poster board or a block of wood for small groups (samples provided on page 47). Those made of poster board can be taped to the student's desk or table. As each of the buttons is introduced, a sticker is added to represent that button. The sample remotes can also be copied on card stock and taped to each students desk.

Teachers or leaders can select the activities that they feel are appropriate for the grade level, class or group size, budget, and time available for this program.

It is advantageous to have an individual specifically trained in implementing this program come into the classroom once a week to work with the kids. It can add interest and appeal to have a guest in the classroom. The teacher can then reinforce the activities as he/she deems appropriate.

This program is designed for the third and fourth grade level. Some of the activities will have to be modified for older or younger age groups.

Provide information for parents about the program and the remote control concept so they can reinforce these skills at home.

This material can also be used in small group settings or in an individual counseling setting. Most activities and handouts can be modified for use outside of the classroom.

▼ Channel Changer ▲

The channel changer button teaches children to filter out distractions by helping them to recognize when they have "changed channels." The remote control provides a visual aid to help them learn to refocus on the task that is most important.

 New Terminology: "What channel are you on?" is another way of saying, "pay attention." When the teacher wants the class to listen, he/she can say "Put your channel on me."

 The Distraction Game: The "Hunter" storybook is read to the class. The students are instructed to listen carefully to the book, because a test (provided on page 10) will be given afterward. Prizes or other incentives can be offered to make it more fun! While the book is being read, the teacher or leader tries to create distractions. When the teacher does this, it gives him/her an opportunity to do the things the students typically do that are a distraction to others. For example: tapping pencils, whispering, giggling, sharpening pencils, going out of the room, passing notes, talking, or anything that might make the class laugh. The students have to try to stay focused on the story. This activity accomplishes several objectives; it helps the kids learn to filter out distractions and shows them how distracting some of their behaviors are to other students. It also introduces the class to *Hunter and His Amazing Remote Control.*

Name _____

Distraction Game Test

Hunter and His Amazing Remote Control
(Instructions located on page 9)

1. Hunter's brain was like a _____.
   a) video game
   b) t.v.
   c) coach's brain

2. What happened to Hunter when he did something without thinking first?
   a) His favorite video fast forwarded to the end.
   b) He knocked over the bookshelf.
   c) He threw a pillow into the air and broke the lamp.

3. Hunter's little brother Josh _____.
   a) took the remote control
   b) got irritated with Hunter because he changed the t.v. channel a lot
   c) took Hunter's baseball and put it on his bookshelf

4. Which of these is not a button on Hunter's remote control?
   a) rewind
   b) stop
   c) fast forward

5. What did Hunter make his remote control out of?
   a) An old t.v. remote control
   b) A pencil box
   c) A block of wood

6. Hunter used his slow motion button _____.
   a) at a birthday party
   b) at a baseball game
   c) when he was in math class

7. Which of the following is a negative thought?
   a) Don't give up!
   b) I need to be more careful next time.
   c) I never do anything right!

8. What happened when Hunter forgot to use his remote control?
   a) He asked his mom for help.
   b) He got a bad case of the "shoulds".
   c) Coach Cooper was disappointed in him.

9. Hunter learned to "zap" away _____.
   a) negative thoughts
   b) distractions
   c) mistakes

10. The "way to go" button was Hunter's _____.
    a) own idea
    b) mom's idea
    c) coach's idea

Pause
|||

The pause button is primarily a transitional button for the fast forward, rewind, slow motion, and coach buttons. This button teaches kids to stop action in order to think, relax, slow down, wait, identify feelings, and create a plan.

 New Terminology: When the leader or teacher says "pause," kids have to stop immediately. Rewards can be given periodically when this is done correctly.

 The Pause Game (provided on the page 15): Students are instructed to do and say certain things. If the instruction is consistent with classroom rules, they are to do it. If they are instructed to do or say something inappropriate, they are to say "pause" and push their pause button. This gives students the opportunity to practice the pause concept and reinforces classroom rules.

 Naming the colors* (provided on page 16): A poster is made with the names of colors; each of the color names is written in a different color. For example, the word "red" is written with a green marker, "yellow" is written with a red marker, "black" is written in blue. Include some color names written in that color ("red" written in red marker). Students are instructed to name the colors, NOT READ THE WORDS, in the order they appear on the poster--as fast as they can. The activity is difficult

Pause

because the written words interfere with the process of identifying the color. Students must use the pause button to prevent from saying the words written. This activity helps teach young people the difference between reacting out of habit and responding appropriately. *

 Practicing patience: The pause button is also used to help kids learn to take turns and wait patiently. Children can practice standing like statues or store mannequins.

 Read the "Hunter" storybook as a class: Have students take turns reading *Hunter and His Amazing Remote Control*. One student reads until the leader says "pause," then the book is passed to the next reader. This provides both reinforcement for the "pause" concept and another opportunity to review the "Hunter" story.

* (This activity is based on *The Stroop Effect* a phenomenon first published by John Ridley Stroop in 1935)

The Pause Game

(Instructions provided on page 13)

1. Stand up
2. Turn around
3. Stand on one foot
4. **Yell really loud**
5. Sit down
6. **Lean back in your chair**
7. Raise your hand
8. **Hit your desk really hard**
9. Stand up
10. Shake hands with the person next to you
11. **Stick your tongue out at the person next to you**
12. **Stand on your desk**
13. Pat yourself on the head
14. Pat your head and rub your stomach
15. Pat your head, rub your stomach and turn around in a circle
16. Pat your stomach, rub your head and turn around in a circle
17. Pat your stomach, rub your head and stand on one foot
18. Pat your head, rub your stomach and stand on one foot
19. **Pat your head, rub your stomach and kick your desk**
20. Sit down
21. Close your eyes
22. **Go to sleep**
23. Open your eyes
24. Smile

Naming the Colors

(Instructions provided on page 13)

red   blue   orange   yellow

black   green   purple   yellow

blue   red   black   orange

purple   yellow   red   green

black   blue   purple   orange

red   yellow   blue   green

black   purple   yellow   blue

The fast forward button on the remote control gives children a tool to remind them to think before they act. Used with the pause button, the concept of looking into the future and imagining what might happen teaches impulsive kids the advantages of evaluating consequences before acting.

 DVDs: Select DVDs that show something wrong because the character didn't evaluate the consequences before acting (these are not hard to find). Use the pause button on the remote to pause the DVD right before the character makes the choice to act (borrowing something valuable, doing something dangerous or dishonest, disobeying authority). Ask children to guess what will happen, or if it is a popular DVD they have seen, allow them to tell what happens. Use the fast forward button on the remote control to move ahead in the DVD to show the consequence. Discuss how the character could have used his/her pause and fast forward buttons. Using an actual remote control in this activity reinforces the concept of the "personal" remote control.

 Checkers: This game is relatively simple to access or make, and most kids already know how to play. It gives kids a "hands on" experience with the mental process of evaluating consequences before acting.

 What will happen next?: Allow students to come up with their own examples of kids or adults who didn't use their fast forward button. Discuss how these individuals might have used their fast forward button.

 How might this person feel?: For social skills training, the concept of empathy can be incorporated into the fast forward training. Give examples of situations where someone said or did something without thinking, resulting in the hurting of another person either physically or emotionally. Help children to understand the impact their words and actions have on others.

The rewind button encourages children to make a cognitive shift from the focus on past failure to future behavioral change. This button teaches students to evaluate their past behavior for the purpose of learning from their mistakes, rather than using past performance as a measure of self-worth. Students can be reminded that everyone makes mistakes and there is no value in getting stuck in the "should" mentality. This button will transition into the coach concept. This can be pointed out to the students so they will be prepared to make the connection between these two concepts when the coach button is discussed.

 Posters: A poster can be made for the classroom showing the change from focus on past failure to an emphasis on future improvement (sample provided on page 21). Students can make their own poster about changing "I shouldn't have..." or "I should have..." to "Next time I'll try to..." or "Everyone makes mistakes."

 The Changing of the "Shoulds": Cut "should" statements (provided on page 22) so each child can choose one from a basket or other container as it is passed around. Instruct children to change the statement to a "Next time..." statement.

 Do-overs: This is basically a second chance. The teacher can say to the student, "would you like to rewind and try a do-over." This gives the

child an opportunity to rehearse appropriate behavior immediately after being corrected. This is an example of how the strategies that teachers are already practicing on a regular basis can be incorporated into the remote control concept.

 Famous "Failures": Share examples of famous people who failed many times on their way to success. Examples are provided on page 26. The teacher or leader can also share a time when he/she failed and had to learn from his/her mistake.

The Changing of the "Shoulds" Cards

(Instructions provided on page 19)

I should not have gone in front of that car on my bike.	I should not have left my bike out in the street.
I should not have gotten mad and quit the basketball team.	I should not show off to impress my friends.
I should take better care of my things.	I should not have broken the lamp.

The Changing of the "Shoulds" Cards

(Instructions provided on page 19)

I should have made a better grade on my test.	I should have done all my homework.
I should not have gotten so mad at my friend.	I should have remembered to bring home my social studies book.
I should not have talked bad about my classmate.	I should not talk so much in class.

The Changing of the "Shoulds" Cards

(Instructions provided on page 19)

I should have more friends.	I should not have eaten so much candy at the party.
I should pay attention better in class.	I should not have gotten so mad and said those things to Mom.
I should not get so mad at my sister.	I should not have watched t.v. when my homework wasn't done.

The Changing of the "Shoulds" Cards

(Instructions provided on page 19)

I should not have made such a a mess in the kitchen.	I should have read the directions on the test.
I should not have spent all of my money.	I should not have said that to my teacher.
I should not rush through my work all of the time. It's messy!	I should not have hit my brother.

Famous Failures

(Instructions provided on page 20)

Michael Jordan

was cut from his high school basketball team.

Ludwig Beethoven's

music teacher said he was "hopeless" as a composer.

Walt Disney

went bankrupt several times before building Disneyland.

Albert Einstein

didn't speak until he was four and
didn't read until he was seven years old.

Henry Ford

failed in business five times before finally succeeding.

Babe Ruth

not only set the record for home runs, but also
set the record for strikeouts.

Abraham Lincoln

lost eight elections, and failed in business
before being elected President.

The slow motion button involves more than just slowing down and being more careful. This button can be used to teach stress management skills such as the identification and appropriate expression of feelings, and relaxation training.

 New Terminology: The teacher can say "We all need to use our slow motion buttons," when the class needs to calm down. For example, when getting ready to leave at the end of the day or lining up for lunch.

 Games: There are several popular children's games that require slow careful movements. These games involve pulling pieces out of a stacked tower until it falls down or taking small pieces out with tweezers. These games can be used to give kids practice in moving slowing and carefully. Spaghetti (uncooked) can be used as a game of "pick-up-sticks" where children try to remove a noodle without moving any other "sticks." Stacking dominoes is another way of practicing slow and careful movements. Several of these games could be set up in stations around the room.

 Relaxation Training: (A) Teach students to take a slow deep breath while counting to ten, breathing in 1-2-3-4-5, breathing out 6-7-8-9-10. Demonstrate by raising up fingers slowly as you inhale and exhale. Tell students that their breathing should be silent and the room should be very quiet during this activity. This should be done at least three times initially, then reinforced periodically. (B) Teach students the difference

between relaxed muscles and tense muscles; have them practice tensing their muscles then relaxing them. (C) Teach visualization; have students imagine they are floating down a slow, gentle river on a raft. Use soft music or nature sounds if they are available.

 How Would You Feel If...?: Help students to increase their vocabulary of feeling words, by adding to the list on page 29. Then encourage them to use this vocabulary to match feelings with experiences, see page 30. Assign each student one of these situations and ask them to select one or more feelings that a person might have in that situation.

 Dealing with Feelings?: Teach children the importance of dealing with their feelings in an appropriate manner. The following activities can be used to help kids express their feelings. (A) Teach kids to blow their feelings into balloons. Use blue balloons for sad feelings, red-angry, yellow-happy, green-jealous, and other colors for nervous, worried, guilty, etc. (B) Use toilet paper squares to represent feelings. Kids can tear off squares to represent their unpleasant feelings and later flush any of those feelings that they want to change. The toilet paper roll can be passed around so children can tear off their own squares and write or draw on them. Limit each child to six squares to maintain control of this activity. (C) Kids should be encouraged to talk to others about their feelings, this can be included in the above activities. These activities are most effective in a well supervised, small group setting.

Feelings Vocabulary

(Instructions provided on page 28)

grouchy	exhausted
pleased	disappointed
scared	worried
embarrassed	proud
silly	contented
thoughtful	overwhelmed
confused	miserable
lonely	capable
successful	enthusiastic
hopeful	hopeless
hurt	mean
surprised	shy
upset	impatient
frustrated	friendly
confident	cheerful
irritated	guilty
anxious	jealous
excited	angry

Matching Feelings with Experiences
(Instructions provided on page 28)

1. Someone made fun of your new haircut?
2. You couldn't find the money you got from your grandmother?
3. Your best friend moved to another state?
4. You were accused of doing something you did not do?
5. Your favorite jacket was stolen?
6. You scored the most points at the basketball game?
7. You couldn't understand how to do your homework?
8. You had an argument with your best friend?
9. It snowed and you got the day off from school?
10. You stained your new shirt with grape juice?
11. You rode out in front of a car on your bike and almost got hit?
12. Your teacher set up a meeting with your parents?
13. You made a 100 on your math test?
14. You found out you were going to get to go camping over the weekend?
15. You had to wait a long time at the doctor's office?
16. You were chosen as "Student of the Month?"
17. You made a big mess in the garage and had to clean it up?
18. You had to go to the hospital to have an operation?
19. Your pet died?
20. Your little brother got into your room and messed up all your things?
21. You dropped your lunch tray at school and spilled food everywhere?
22. You won $25.00 in a poster contest?
23. You lied to your father about something you did?
24. You had to go to a new school where you didn't know anyone?
25. You got to go to an amusement park?

Self-instruction is an important skill for children to learn. The focus of the coach button is on problem-solving strategies. The activities are designed to teach students how to break down a task into smaller components, develop a plan, organize and schedule their life, and encourage themselves in the process.

 Coach's Playbook of Winning Strategies: This can be a small notebook containing rules, schedules for assignments and tests, a plan for after school responsibilities or a checklist of items that need to be taken home or brought from home (sample provided on page 33). Teachers could spend the last few minutes of each school day helping kids to put the necessary information in their notebook. Parents could be included in this activity. At home they could say "Why don't you get your playbook and tell me what your plan is for this afternoon (or evening)?" The use of the playbook can be modified to accommodate the needs of each teacher and class.

 Divide and Organize (exercise provided on page 34): Have kids organize smaller tasks under the larger job heading. Discuss which job they would do first. This activity helps the children to learn sequencing and time management.

**Coach**

Problem-Solving (exercise provided on page 36): Teach students basic problem-solving skills:
1. Identifying the problem.
2. Getting the facts.
3. Brainstorming possible solutions.
4. Choosing the best solution (exercise provided on page 36). Divide children into small groups, give each group a problem to solve using the skills learned. Allow a spokesperson for each group to share their solutions.

Coaching examples: Show videos that demonstrate good coaching methods. Invite a coach to class who is familiar with the concepts of the remote control. Ask him/her to discuss the importance of encouragement, problem-solving ability, being organized, and not giving up on yourself.

The Coach's Playbook

(Instructions provided on page 31)

1. "The Rules of the Game" - You can't be a great athlete or coach if you don't know and follow the rules.

2. "Stuff to Do" - Make lists of assignments, goals and daily reminders.

3. "Winning Strategies" - Learn techniques for problem-solving, planning and breaking down tasks.

4. "Team Talk" - A place for communication between parent, teacher and student.

5. "Way to Go Journal" - Leave space in the coach's play book for this exercise.

Divide and Organize

(Additional instructions provided on page 31)

Write the tasks below on 3 x 5 cards. Make enough sets of cards so that groups of three students will each have a set to organize.

Tell the students: It is the beginning of Spring Break and you have to do the following things this week.

1. Clean your room
2. Get ready for a party
3. Study for an important spelling contest (Saturday Morning)
4. Plant a Garden

On each card is a task that has to be done by 7:00 Friday night, when you will have a party. The spelling contest will be Saturday morning. You have from Monday to Friday to complete these tasks. Do the following:

1. Organize each task, according to the project it falls under.. For example, "make the bed" goes in the "Clean your room" stack. You should have four stacks.
2. For each of the four projects, organize the cards according to which task should be done first. For example, "decide what to plant" comes before "buy seeds."
3. Decide which day to do each task. For example: Monday - "write and mail invitations" Friday - "prepare party food." You should have five stacks, one for each day of the week.
4. You now know what you have to do each day in order to get all four projects done during Spring Break.

Tasks:

Pick up stuff from the bedroom floor. Clean out closet. Clean out from under the bed. Put game pieces back in game box. Stack games on shelf in closet. Put DVDs back in boxes. Stack DVDs on the shelf. Vacuum bedroom floor.

Decide who to invite. Write out and mail invitations. Decide on what food to have at the party. Go to the grocery store. Prepare party food. Set up volleyball net outside. Find the volleyball in the garage. Set out food and drinks for guests.

Find list of spelling words. Write down all the spelling words three times. Spell the words out loud. Make sentences using the spelling words. Ask someone to give you a practice test on the words. Write down all the words that you missed on the practice test. Ask someone to give you a second practice test.

Decide what to plant. Purchase seeds. Prepare soil for planting. Read seeds packages to learn how deep to plant the seeds. Plant seeds. Water garden. Water garden again. Water garden again.

Coach

Problem-Solving Exercise
"Use the Coach button when you have problems"
(Instructions provided on page 32)

1. John is having a hard time understanding the math homework. He tries to listen in class, but he can't seem to figure out what to do when he gets home. He usually ends up guessing and then makes a low grade on his home work and the test.

2. Michelle is really shy. She feels nervous when she has to talk to people and sometimes she has a hard time thinking of things to say. She wants to have friends, but the other kids don't know that. Some of them think she doesn't like them because she never smiles at them or says "hi."

3. Jake has an older brother who seems to be good at everything. It seems like he's always winning awards for grades and sports. He has lots of friends and almost never gets in trouble. Jake feels like he can't do anything very well and feels jealous when his brother gets a lot of attention.

4. Zack has a hard time concentrating in class. It seems like he's always got something important on his mind, like worrying about his older sister who's been getting into a lot of trouble lately. Zack's grades have been going down lately because he daydreams so much.

5. Mark and Joe are next door neighbors. They have been friends for years. Joe has gone to a private school until this year. Now he is in the same class as Mark. The other guys in class think Joe is weird because he acts a little different. Mark's friends at school do not want Joe to be part of their group. Mark feels sorry for Joe, but wants to be with his school friends.

6. Jan has forgotten to bring her book home from school and will not be able to do her homework tonight. Lately, she has been forgetting a lot of things, like giving her dog fresh water, packing a lunch for school, and giving her mom the note about the school music program.

7. Scott has a friend that comes over to his house sometimes. This friend is a lot of fun, but he messes things up a lot, then Scott has to clean up. He is also careless with Scott's things and has broken some stuff.

8. Jill's friends have all stolen something from a store at the mall. They tell her she should do it too because its the popular thing to do to prove your "cool." They tell her it's "no big deal" and assure her that she won't get caught. She really doesn't want to but she wants her friends to quit bugging her about it.

This button teaches students to recognize and reject unpleasant thinking patterns and irrational beliefs.

 Self-Talk: Teach children that they are always talking to themselves inside their head. Explain that everyone struggles with negative "self-talk" (even adults). Give several examples (samples found on page 41).

 Irrational Beliefs: Teach children how to recognize overgeneralized and and exaggerated beliefs. Give several examples (samples found on page 41).

 Zap that Thought!: The teacher or leader reads "thoughts" (provided on page 42) out loud, and students try to decide if the thought is unpleasant. If they think it is unpleasant, they say "zap." Students will have to be reminded to use their pause button if they are tempted to say "zap" before the teacher is finished reading the thought. Students could also be given a coach's whistle to use for this game. They could blow the whistle rather than saying "zap" to call a "thought penalty."

 Sidewalk Chalk: Write unpleasant thoughts on the sidewalk and allow kids to take turns using a large water gun to wash them away. Remind them to use their pause buttons while waiting their turn.

 Give Them a Name and Face: Create characters to represent unpleasant thoughts--Not Good Enough Norman, Can't Do Anything Right Rita, Stupid Sal, Just Give Up Jerry, Nobody Likes Me Larry. Allow students to choose a character to draw and display their pictures around the room. For a later activity, have the students turn the paper over and change the characters into positive personalities such as Never Give Up Norman, Responsible Rita, Smart Enough Sal, Just Try Your Best Jerry, Friendly Larry.

Unhealthy Thinking

(Instructions provided on page 39)

Negative "Self-Talk"

Thinking you're "not good enough".
Comparing yourself to others.
Being overly critical; focusing on what you do wrong.
Telling yourself you can't do things before you have tried hard enough.
The wrong way to coach yourself.

Overgeneralization

Just because something has happened before, it doesn't mean that it will always happen in the future.
Just because something has not happened yet, it doesn't mean that it will never happen.

Zapper

Zap that Thought

(Instructions provided on page 39)

1. *Everyone has to like me, if someone doesn't like me it means there's something wrong with me.*

2. Not everyone is going to like me.

3. *It is terrible and awful to make a mistake.*

4. Everyone makes mistakes.

5. *If you think you might fail at something, it's better to just quit trying.*

6. It's OK to fail at something, it means you were willing to try something that was hard for you.

7. *I will only be happy if everything happens the way I think it should.*

8. I can be happy, even when things go wrong.

9. *Other people make me angry.*

10. I get angry sometimes when others do and say things that I don't like.

11. *I'm just not a lucky person.*

12. Some people seem to have more advantages than others.

13. *If my parents really cared about me, they would always let me do what I want to do.*

14. I won't always get to do what I want to do.

15. *If I blame things on other people, it will make me seem better.*

16. If I take responsibility for my mistakes and say "I'm sorry," it will make me feel better about myself.

17. *If I can't learn to do something quickly, it is probably too hard for me and I should just quit trying.*

18. Some things will be hard for me to learn to do.

19. *I just can't handle it when things don't seem fair.*

20. When things don't seem fair and there is nothing that I can do about it, I can handle it.

21. *I would get better grades, if I had a better teacher.*

22. I won't always like the way my teacher does things.

23. *If someone doesn't agree with me, they probably don't like me.*

24. Good friends disagree sometimes.

25. *If I could have a lot of money or stuff, I would be happy.*

26. You have to be happy with yourself.

27. *Winning is most important, even if you have to lie or cheat to do it.*

28. Winning is fun.

29. *If my teacher liked me more, she would have given me a better grade.*

30. If I had worked harder, I might have made a better grade.

31. *If a lot of people around me are doing something, it must be the right thing to do.*

32. There are a lot of people who do dangerous or mean things in order to feel more important or to get other people to like him.

Way to Go!

This button will teach kids positive self-talk. The Way to Go activities help students to identify and focus on their strengths, and credit themselves for effort, positive attitude, improvement and achievement of goals.

 Way to Go Journal: Children can keep a notebook where they write down the things they do right. Focusing not just on achievement, but effort, attitude and improvement. This can be incorporated into the Coaches Playbook.

 Letter of Affirmation: Teachers, parents and other class members (draw names to decide who will write to who) can write letters stating the positive qualities they see in the student. Parents and other students should be given guidelines so each child will have a positive experience with this activity (provided on page 46).

Way to Go!

Letter of Affirmation
(Instructions provided on page 45)

Dear Parent,

On _____ we will be talking about the importance of noticing the positive things we do and affirming ourselves. So often, kids do not focus on their accomplishments and strengths.

This will be an opportunity for each child in the class to feel good about who they are and what they have accomplished. Please participate in this experience by writing a special letter of affirmation and encouragement to your child. You may want to include the following in your letter:

Positive personality characteristics that you see in him or her. Here are some examples: caring, hard worker, good decision maker, calm, cooperative, courageous, curious, easy-going, flexibility, generous, enthusiastic, perceptiveness, honesty, patient, creative, desires to learn new things, friendly, always thinking of a new idea, cautious, openness, fun, independent, sense of humor. Give examples of times when you have noticed these things.

Statements that are just affirmations of "being" not necessarily focused on anything that they have done. For example:
"I'm so lucky to have you for a son or daughter.
"I love spending time with you."
"I like to hear your ideas."

The letter can be any length. If you would like assistance writing it or need a sample letter, please let me know. Please have your letter to me by _____. If you can keep it a secret, it will be a nice surprise for him or her. No one else will read it. You can put it in a small envelope with his or her name on it, then inside a larger envelope with my name on it, or just bring it right to me at school.

Thank you for participating.

"A Message from Hunter" can be used in any way the teacher/leader thinks is appropriate. It can be a motto that the students recite or part of the Playbook. The purpose of this is to use the remote control idea to reinforce and teach the concept of internal locus of control.

A Message from Hunter

Remember...

- Things won't always work out the way you want them to.

- You can't change what has already happened.

- You won't always be treated nicely by other people.

- You will make mistakes sometimes.

- You will have to do some things that you don't want to do.

- You won't always get what you want.

- Some things will be really hard for you to do.

- You can't control what other people do and say.

BUT... You CAN use your remote control !!!

- No one else has a remote control to make you think, act or feel in a certain way.

- You are the only one who can make your remote control work.

Reproducible Remote Control Covers

Below are two remote control covers that you may want to copy on cardstock and provide to each child. These can be taped onto the top of the students' desk and as each button is discussed, colored with crayons.

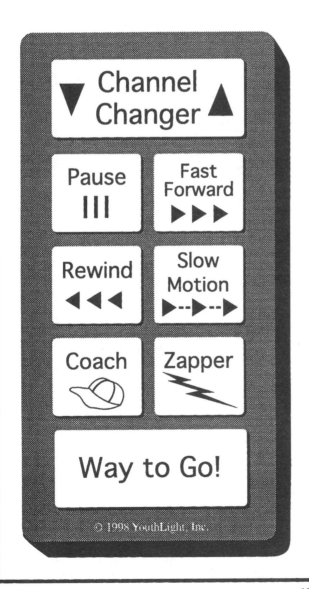

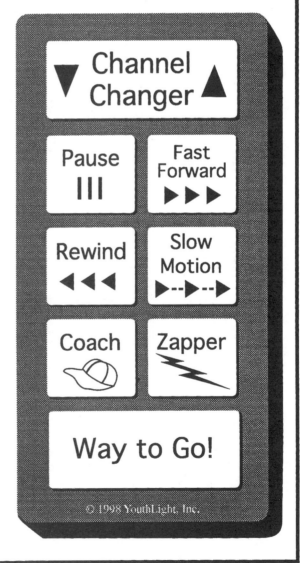

Hunter and His Amazing Remote Control

Part B: Storybook

Written & illustrated by Lori Copeland, Ph.D.

Hunter was a really amazing kid. He was smart, creative and full of ideas that most kids would probably never think of.

He had lots of energy and enthusiasm so he really liked sports, art, and all kinds of games.

Hunter always noticed everything that was going on around him. His mind took everything in because he didn't want to miss anything.

He filled his mind with so much information that he always had something interesting to think about. Hunter's brain was like a T.V. with lots of channels.

Often, Hunter felt frustrated by the way his brain worked. Sometimes, when he was in class trying to listen to his teacher explain the lesson, his mind switched to a different channel.

Then he would make mistakes later, because he missed some important information while he was on that channel.

He also felt frustrated with all of his energy and enthusiasm. Sometimes, he did things without thinking first, and he really got into a mess. Like the time he threw a pillow into the air and broke the lamp!

Sometimes, when he was supposed to be still, he felt like he had so much energy inside that he might explode if he didn't get to move around soon.

Other people got frustrated with Hunter too. He was so tired of hearing "sit still," "pay attention," "relax," "listen," and "use your head!"

At times, he felt like there was something wrong with him, because he forgot that these frustrations were part of his specialness---part of being so smart, creative, energetic, and enthusiastic.

These special talents and frustrations were all part of being Hunter.

One day, when Hunter was watching his favorite T.V. program, his little brother, Josh, picked up the remote control and started changing channels.

This irritated Hunter so he took the remote control from Josh and used it to return to his program.

Suddenly, Hunter had one of his amazing ideas. "I need a remote control for my brain!" exclaimed Hunter. So, he set out to make one.

He took a block of wood and his markers and made a "channel changer." He practiced using it to keep his attention focused on only one thing at a time.

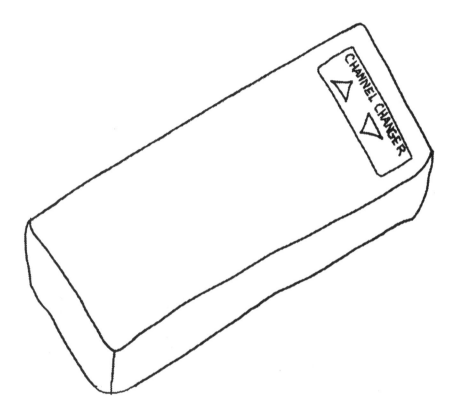

When he felt his mind changing channels (like in Math class when he started thinking about what he was going to eat for lunch), he used his remote control to change back to the channel that he was supposed to be on.

Hunter found that the more he used his remote control, the better it worked.

His teacher even noticed the difference.

One day Hunter was watching his favorite movie about a kids' hockey team. Once again, Josh got the remote control. He pushed "pause" first, then "fast forward."

By the time Hunter got the remote control back, his movie was near the end---right at his favorite part where a good coach leads his team in a championship game. The winning point is shown in slow motion, and the movie ends with players celebrating the hard work and positive attitude that helped to make them a great team.

As Hunter reached for the remote control to turn off the movie, he realized that there was so much more he could do with his own remote control. He began to think of buttons that he could add.

The first button Hunter added was "pause." He learned to push this button before he did or said something that could get him into trouble. He tried to use "pause" before he threw something in the house, before he spoke out in class, and before he ran out into the street without looking.

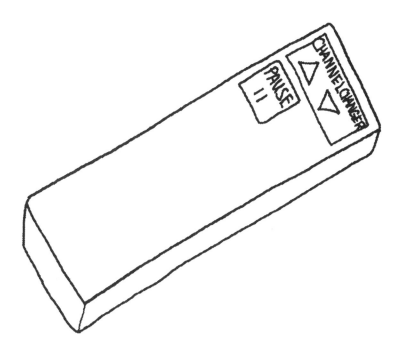

Using "pause" gave Hunter a chance to think before he did something. At first, it was really hard to remember to use the "pause" button on his remote control, but the more he practiced, the easier it got.

As Hunter was learning to use the "pause" button, he remembered that "fast forward" on the remote control allowed him to see what happens later in the movie. He decided that he would put a "fast forward" button on his remote control to help him see into the future.

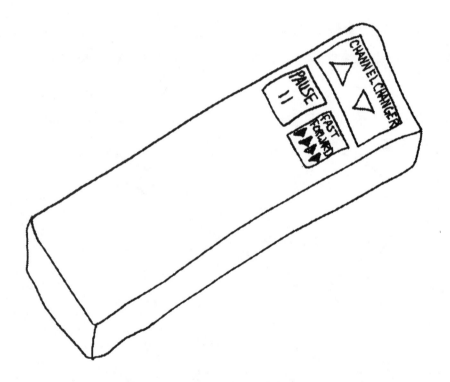

He used it the next day as he was about to stand on Josh's bookshelf to reach the football. He pushed "pause" then "fast forward" and realized that the bookshelf might fall over on him. He decided to go ask his mother for help instead.

Mom was really impressed that he was learning to ask for help when he needed it.

But even with lots of practice, Hunter didn't always remember to push the "pause" and "fast forward" buttons before he did or said something, and ...

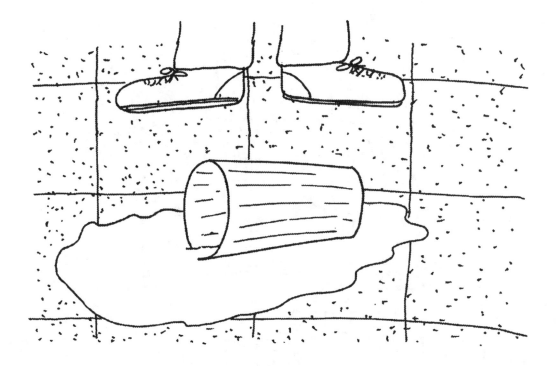

DISASTER!

Of course, everyone makes mistakes, even the most amazing people. But when Hunter messed up...

...he got a bad case of the SHOULDS. He would say to himself, "I should have said something else" "I should have done something different" "I should not have done that" or "I should be more careful".

The SHOULDS always made him feel discouraged.

Should   Should

Should   Should

Mom got the SHOULDS too sometimes!

Once, after a bad case of the SHOULDS, Hunter got an idea..."If I had a rewind button, I could go back to where I was before I messed up and think about what I could have done differently. Then maybe next time, it will be easier to make a better choice."

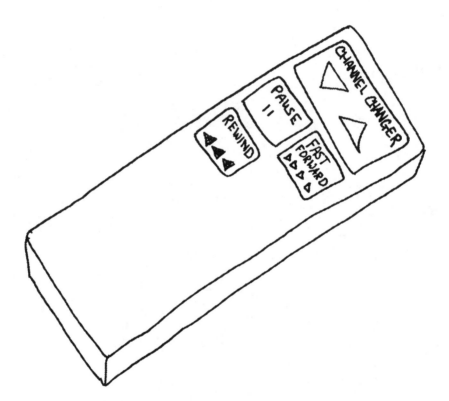

Mom liked the idea and sometimes she let Hunter use "rewind" to say or do something over---before he got in trouble. It was like getting a second chance and it sure helped.

Hunter loved to drink Fizzola Cola, because it had lots of bubbles. One day, he asked his mom to put a can of Fizzola Cola in his lunch box for school. Mom said...

"OK Hunter, but remember, you can't shake it around like juice or punch. You have to be more careful with Fizzola Cola."

By lunch time, Hunter had forgotten to be more careful with his lunch box. He threw it up in the air three times, but caught it only once. Then he swung his lunch back and forth while he waited in line. When he finally opened up the can of Fizzola Cola, it sprayed everywhere.

The lunchroom attendant was not pleased!

When Hunter got home that day, he told his mom what had happened at lunch. Mom said... "Hunter, I think people are kind of like drinks. Some people are serious and sophisticated like tea. Other people are like fruit punch - sweet and cheerful all of the time. Then there are the Fizzola Cola people, full of excitement and fun, but when they get "shaken up," they have to learn to calm down so they don't "blow up." What kind of person do you think you are, Hunter?"

They laughed, because they both knew the answer to that question.

So Hunter decided to use his remote control to help him when he had a little too much energy. He made a "slow motion" button to remind him to move a lot slower and become more relaxed.

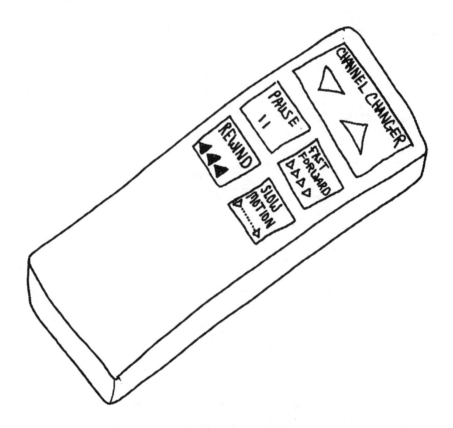

He learned that if he took a slow deep breath as he pushed "slow motion," and then counted to ten slowly, it worked even better.

He used "slow motion" at his birthday party when he was opening his presents. "I'm really glad I slowed down," he thought later, "It gave me a chance to thank everyone, and it made the fun last a lot longer."

One of Hunter's favorite people was Coach Cooper, his baseball coach. Coach Cooper seemed to know just what to say to encourage the team members to try their hardest. One day, Hunter struck out three times, dropped the ball again and again, and tripped over second base all in one game.

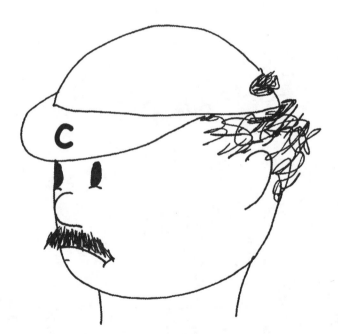

Hunter was ready to quit the team...Until,

Coach Cooper explained that all great athletes have bad days now and then--- especially when they are young and still learning. He encouraged Hunter to keep trying and learn from his mistakes. He also helped Hunter think of some ways he could improve his game.

Later that evening, Hunter thought, " I wish that I had Coach Cooper around all of the time."

That was how the "Coach" button became part of the remote control.

Hunter pushed "Coach" when he needed encouragement to try harder. He pushed "Coach" when he needed to remember that it's O.K. to make mistakes, and he pushed "Coach" when he needed to come up with a plan for doing better.

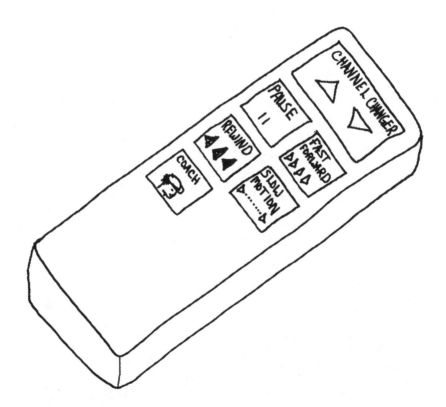

The "Coach" button was just what Hunter needed not just in sports, but on the playground, in class and at home.

© YouthLight, Inc.

Sometimes, Hunter had a negative thought. A negative thought is a discouraging, unkind, or hurtful thought like... "There's something wrong with me." "I'm not smart enough" "People don't like me" "I'm a bad kid" "I'll never get it right" "I'm just not good enough".

These thoughts are almost always wrong, but if we are not careful, we can start believing them.

So Hunter put a "zapper" button on his remote control to zap away those negative thoughts before he had a chance to believe them.

The last button on Hunter's remote control was his Mom's idea. She said to her son, "Hunter, I'm not always around to tell you when you've done something right. So why don't you put a button on it that will remind you to notice when you are successful."

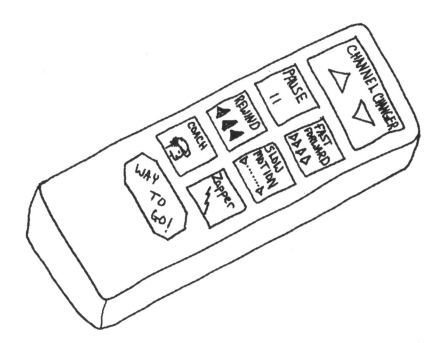

Hunter named it the "Way to Go!" button, and as it turned out, he used it more than he ever thought he would.

Before long, Hunter became so good at using his remote control, that he didn't even need to have it with him. It was as if he had an invisible one with him all of the time.

Hunter understood that he was the only one who could use his remote control. No one else could make him think, feel, or do something. Even when other people did or said things that he didn't like, he could still choose which buttons to push. He realized that everything he did or said was up to him, and he stopped blaming other people (even Josh) for things.

The remote control changed Hunter's life. He got along better with his friends, parents and teachers. He didn't get into trouble as often. He also did better in school. He still made mistakes, and he still got frustrated when he forgot to use his remote control. But the best change of all was that the amazing remote control helped this amazing boy to realize just how amazing he really was.